This book belongs to

MEGAN
....

This edition first published in 2010 by Castle Street Press
an imprint of make believe ideas ltd.

Copyright © 2006 make believe ideas ltd.
The Wilderness, Berkhamsted, Hertfordshire, HP4 2AZ, UK.
565 Royal Parkway, Nashville, TN 37214, USA.

The Bouncing King

Illustrations by Yannick Robert

The happy king
loves bouncing.

Whenever he sees bees
buzzing or lambs
skipping, he starts
to bounce.

People love bouncing with the king. The prime minister bounces as he writes VERY IMPORTANT LAWS.

Only the gremlins can stop the king bouncing. They live in the castle attic.

One day, the king bounces so high that he goes through the ceiling and into the attic. WHACK! He hits his head on the roof and falls down again.

He lands on the prime minister.
Oh NO! There is a gremlin
sitting on the king's shoulder.

"You are not a king!" says the gremlin. "Kings are sensible and wise. Kings do not bounce."

The king is very sad. He sits on the sofa and wears very heavy boots to make sure he cannot bounce.

He makes a VERY IMPORTANT
LAW. No one must ever
bounce again.

There are no ball games, no trampolining, and no space hopping. Everyone is very sad.

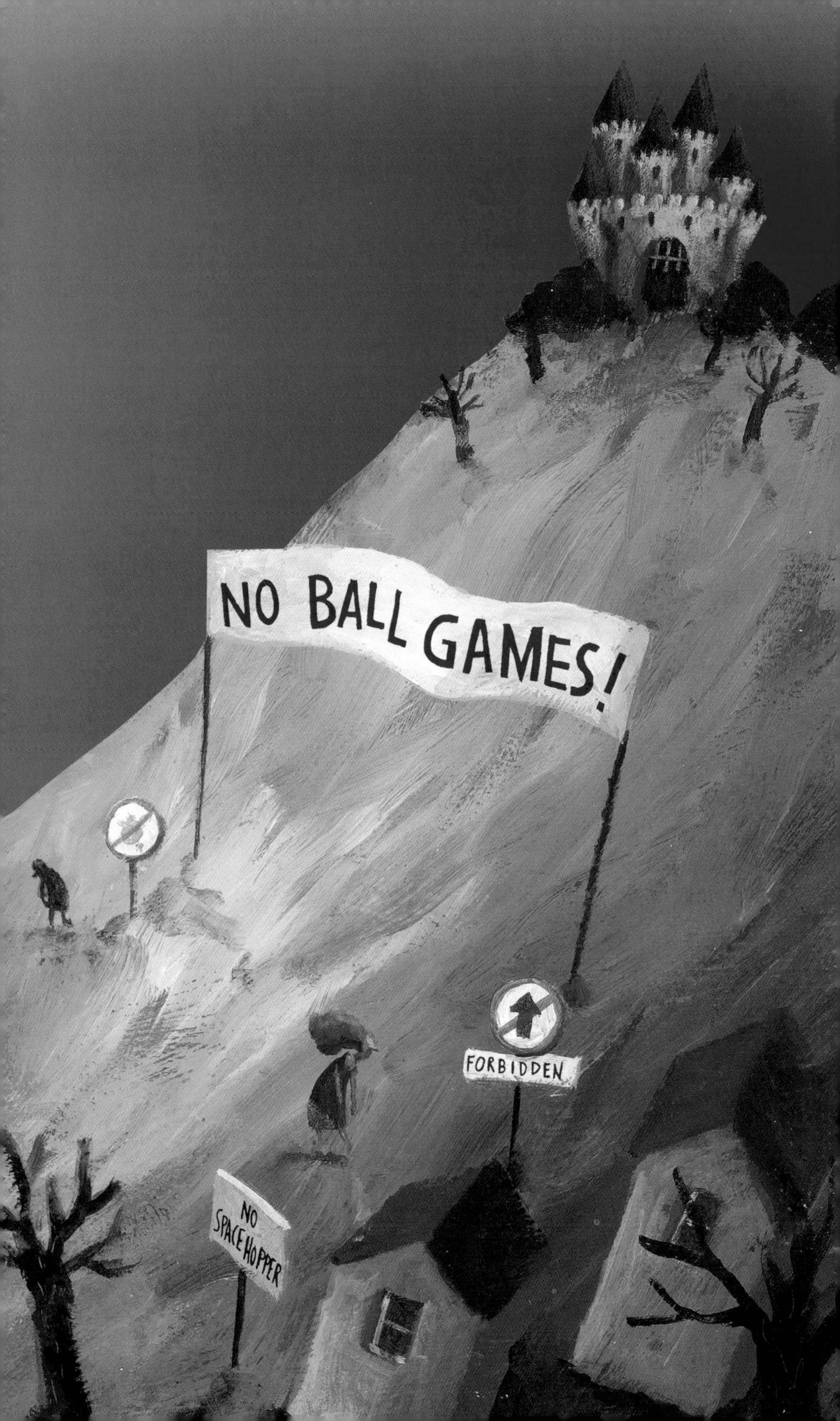
NO BALL GAMES!
FORBIDDEN
NO SPACE HOPPER

The prime minister is puzzled.
He cannot see or hear the
gremlin. But one day he reads
about gremlins.

The prime minister pulls
off the king's heavy boots.
"We are going for a walk!"
he says.

The king feels lighter without
his heavy boots. Everyone is
pleased to see him, and the
king feels happier.

The king sees the flowers growing, the bees buzzing, and the lambs skipping around.

He feels an itch in his feet.
It wriggles up his legs, and
BOING! The king gives a great
bounce, as high as a tree.

The gremlin falls to the ground.
SPLAT! Five lambs land on the
gremlin and squash him flat.

Now the king bounces everywhere again. There is a new VERY IMPORTANT LAW. Every week, the people must go and watch the lambs. This will make everyone want to keep on bouncing.

Ready to tell

Oh no! Some of the pictures from this story have been mixed up! Can you retell the story and point to each picture in the correct order?

Picture dictionary

Encourage your child to read these harder words from the story and gradually develop their basic vocabulary.

attic

bee

bounce

flowers

gremlin

king

lamb

tree

walk

Key words

Here are some key words used in context. Help your child to use other words from the border in simple sentences.

The king likes to **bounce**.

"**No!**" says the gremlin.

He is very sad.

He likes to **see** the lambs.

He bounces **up** high.

Spring sports

If it's a sunny day and you feel happy like the Bouncing King, why not hold a bouncing competition?

You will need
2 lengths of rope • hoops or bean bags • one ball per contestant • one sack or old pillow case per contestant • a "space hopper" (or two if possible)

What to do
Set out your course, using the ropes to mark the "start" and "finish" lines. Here are some races you could plan:

1 Hop It: a hopping race. You could do this in two laps, hopping first on one leg and then on the other.

2 Bounce Around: a bouncing race. Racers have to jump around beanbags or in and out of hoops that you have put in position, bouncing as high and as far as they can.

3 Bouncing Balls: bouncing a ball as you run the course.

4 Sack Race: bounce to the finish line in large sacks or old pillowcases.

5 The Big Bounce: bounce to the finish line on a "space hopper." If you have only one of these toys, ask a grown-up to time contestants to see who is the quickest.

Can you come up with other fun ideas for your own bouncing races? Good luck and happy bouncing!